My India: A Journey of Discovery is a charming book that invites young readers of Indian descent on an exciting journey to discover their homeland: **India**. It prompts children to work through a series of riddles about India's colorful festivals, majestic temples, royal history, delicious food, vibrant music, and mindfulness. But, on the trip, the child faces a hidden twist revealing that it is not just what others tell you or teach you – it is what your thoughts and senses that you associate with the place that makes your homeland special. The story ends with a series of interactive activities for the child to complete that helps them make this story, their own.

This book is part of the **My Homeland** series, which will include titles exploring countries through the eyes of a child traveler, solving riddles that spell out the name of a country, while highlighting elements of the culture. These stories are designed to awaken a child's curiosity about their homeland by preserving or instilling a deep appreciation for the country's natural and cultural wonders. Each volume is a work of art with highly detailed imagery that brings the story to life and sparks the reader's imagination while featuring iconic places of their homeland.

My INDIA
A Journey of Discovery

Written by - **Olivera Jankovska**

Illustrated by - **Sreejith**

My India: A Journey of Discovery
©2020 Atlas Ink, LLC

This is a book designed with a lot of love and support from the
community. Thanks to all who contributed to and
improved this book:

Edits by: Matt Orefice, Ilmar Norvik, Michelle Wanasundera and Swathi Sriram
Art Direction by: Ritesh Sengupta and Daniela Jankovska
Cultural Review by: Tushar Bajaj, Preity Bhagia and Ramya Ranghuram

To my son
Veyaan Bajaj

Iccha's eyes were open wide, she yearned to learn and see,
her story as it extends across the other sea.

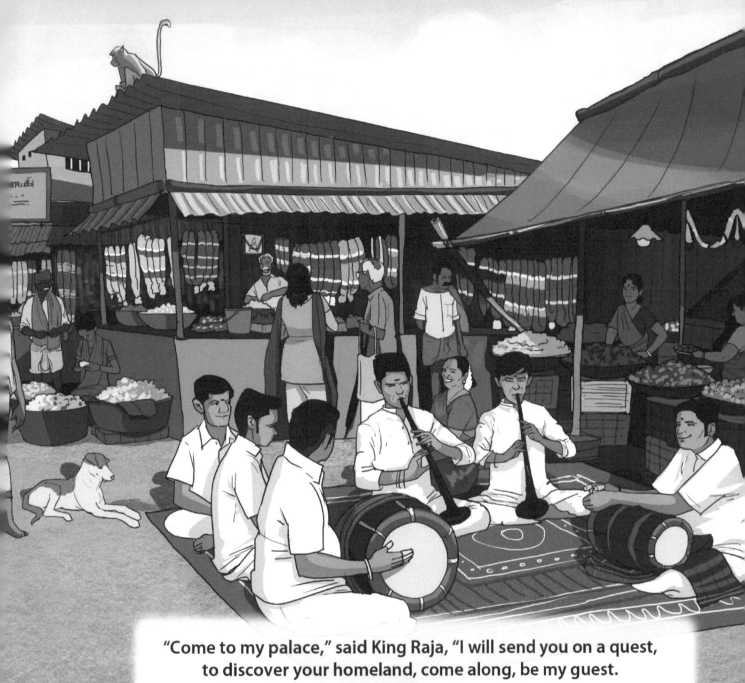

"Come to my palace," said King Raja, "I will send you on a quest,
to discover your homeland, come along, be my guest.
Your challenge is a riddle, made up of five letters,
when you solve it, you'll understand your story so much better."

"So here is my question - it gives a nice full belly,
it's soft, round, and white, but no, it is not jelly.
It tastes like rice and looks like the full moon at night;
it is served with sambar and chutney, you relish it with every bite."

"Oh yes, I know it, it is so yummy,
and I often eat it with my mummy.
The answer is *idli*, and that begins with ' I ',
now I know the first letter, thank you, goodbye!"

Iccha crossed seven towns and seven rivers,
she thought about her next clue and her hint-givers.
Suddenly, she heard bells chiming atop a small green mound,
she walked towards a temple following the enchanting sound.

"Welcome to this lovely place, welcome, Iccha dear,
I'm Nani Rani, and your next hint is right here.
When my hands join like this beside my heart,
my soul greets yours and a conversation we can start."

Rainbows of silky saris dazzled shoppers and cows on busy streets,
and inviting stalls with glazed sweets and spices sprinkled on delicious treats.
But Iccha must keep going, she'd found an 'I', and an 'N',
no stopping or shopping, when only three letters remain.

 "Happy Holi, Mr. Dost! I know, *dhol* drums begin with 'D'!
Thank you for your clue, now I've found the first three."

Iccha had been searching, searching all around,
but the next clue was hidden and nowhere to be found.
There were only two more letters Iccha needs to find,
maybe her family had some good ideas in mind?

Iccha closed her eyes, and then she saw herself, her guide,
"I've got it, it's me! And *Iccha* starts with an 'I'!
My name means 'a wish', the power of 'me' was the key,
I am off to find the last letter, thank you, family!"

Now our Iccha was back on track and this time,
she was walking beside Mahatma Gandhi who eyed a beautiful sign.

"Is that a clock or a lock? Or the rays of the sun glowing?
Iccha, look at the colorful fabric gently flowing.
Within, as the circle spins it unfolds stories with learnings galore,
with a total of twenty-four spokes in it, Iccha, explore!"

"I think that I have solved this exciting riddle,
Ashoka Chakra is the flag wheel in the middle.
Now I know that the puzzle ends with ' A '!
I've discovered so much about my homeland today!
And now it's spelled out in full, I can happily reveal,
that my homeland is **INDIA**, oh how proud I feel!"

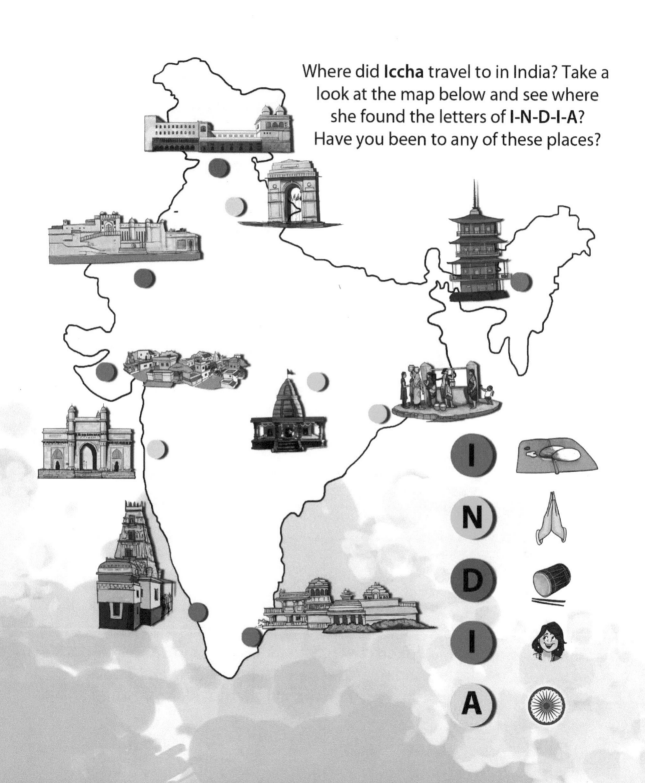

Where did **Iccha** travel to in India? Take a look at the map below and see where she found the letters of **I-N-D-I-A**? Have you been to any of these places?

Let's Play a Name Game

A Ashoka Chakra

B Bollywood

C Chai

D Dhol

E Elephant

F Falooda

G Gandhi

H Holi

I Idli

J Jalebi

K Kulfi

L Lotus Temple

M Mango

N Namaste

O Om

P Peacock

Q Qutubminar

R Rupee

S Sitar

T Taj Mahal

U Ullu

V Veena

W Wicket

X Xacuti

Y Yoga

Z Zero

Use the Indian-themed alphabet above to spell your name using cultural elements of India!

Hello! My name is **Iccha** Idli, Chai, Chai, Holi, Ashoka Chakra

My name is _____ or _____
(please write your name)   (please draw/glue the icons for each letter)

Please visit the author's page at www.atlasink.org for more alphabet options. There, you can also download the alphabet above if you prefer to print and glue the icons of your name.
Have you come up with your own Indian-themed alphabet? Share with us!

Did you notice...

This section includes an interactive activity that asks you to go back through the illustrations in this book and take a close look at elements you may have missed while reading the story. There are ten scenes, one from each page of the story. Primarily, the purpose of this section is to inspire storytelling. It is also an opportunity to grow your curiosity and learn more about India. Additional interactive, as well as creative activities and prompts are available on the author's page at **www.atlasink.org**.

In **illustration 1**, there are musicians. Can you name one of the instruments played?

In **illustration 2**, there is a woman drawing something. What is this art called?

In **illustration 4**, there is a woman making a garland. What are some typical flowers used to make these?

In **illustration 3**, there is a group of children playing a game. What sport is it?

In **illustration 5**,
there is a man cooking at a market.
What is the snack called?

In **illustration 6**,
there is a girl playing with colors at a Holi
festival. Do you know during which
season this festival occurs?

In **illustration 7**,
there is a Buddha statue drawing
inspired by a real place. Do you
know where it is located?

In **illustration 10**,
the 'Chhatrapati Shivaji Maharaj
Terminus' is shown. Do you
know where it is located?

In **illustration 8**,
there are diyas (small lamps)
lined near the table. Do you
know a festival these are
commonly used at?

In **illustration 9**,
there is a man giving a ride to a passenger.
Do you know what the vehicle is called?

Short answers:
*1) Nadaswaram; 2) Kolam or Rangoli; 3) Cricket; 4) Marigold flowers; 5) Bhature;
6) Spring; 7) Buddha Park of Ravangla; 8) Diwali; 9) Cycle rikshaw; 10) Mumbai*

CPSIA information can be obtained
at www.ICGtesting.com
Printed in the USA
LVHW070011101120
671122LV00019B/659